Phonics
Workbook 3

Reading, writing and spelling practice

Learn to read

Focus:
ai ee igh oa oo *oo* ar
or ur ow oi ear air er

Published in the UK by Scholastic, 2023

Scholastic Distribution Centre, Bosworth Avenue, Tournament Fields,
Warwick CV34 6UQ

Scholastic Ireland, 89E Lagan Road, Dublin Industrial Estate, Glasnevin,
Dublin, D11 HP5F

SCHOLASTIC and associated logos are trademarks and/or registered
trademarks of Scholastic Inc.

www.scholastic.co.uk

© 2023, Scholastic

1 2 3 4 5 6 7 8 9   3 4 5 6 7 8 9 0 1 2

A CIP catalogue record for this book is available from the
British Library.

ISBN 978-0702-30946-5

Printed and bound by Leo Paper Products Ltd, China.

The book is made of materials from
well-managed, FSC®-certified forests
and other controlled sources.

Author
Rachel Russ

Editorial team
Rachel Morgan, Vicki Yates, Suzy Beddoes and Jennie Clifford

Design team
Andrea Lewis and Grace Design

Illustration
Becky Down

Contents

How to use this book 4

ai, ee, igh, oa, oo, *oo* 5

ar, or, ur, ow, oi, ear, air, er 12

Tricky word practice 20

Nonsense word practice 21

All sounds practice 22

Certificate 24

What is phonics?

Phonics is a way of teaching children to read and write. It is based around the idea that a sound is represented by a letter or group of letters. For example, the sound **s** is represented by the written letter 's'. Sometimes a sound is represented by more than one letter, for example, 'sh' or 'igh'.

At school, your child will learn sounds and the letters that represent them. They then learn to **blend** sounds together to read simple words, for example, n-igh-t, night. This is sometimes called '**sounding out**' a word. They will learn to write by **segmenting** a word into its individual sounds and then writing the letter or group of letters that represent those sounds.

Some words cannot be read easily by sounding them out but are used very often, for example, 'the'. We call these words **tricky words**. Children are taught to read and write tricky words at school.

How to use this book

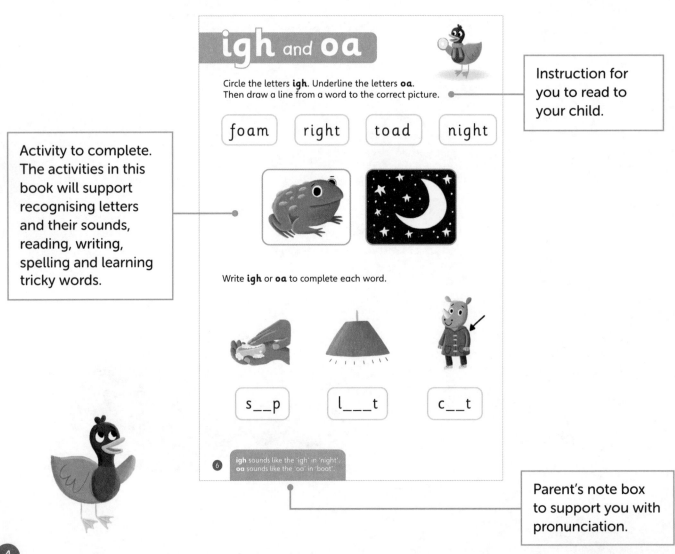

Activity to complete. The activities in this book will support recognising letters and their sounds, reading, writing, spelling and learning tricky words.

Instruction for you to read to your child.

Parent's note box to support you with pronunciation.

(within activity image)

igh and **oa**

Circle the letters **igh**. Underline the letters **oa**.
Then draw a line from a word to the correct picture.

foam   right   toad   night

Write **igh** or **oa** to complete each word.

s__p   l___t   c__t

igh sounds like the 'igh' in 'night'.
oa sounds like the 'oa' in 'boat'.

6

ai and ee

Colour the planets with **ai** words blue.
Colour the planets with **ee** words red.
Then write your own **ai** word and **ee** word in the blank planets.

seed

leek

rail

paid

feet

wait

chain

keep

ai sounds like the 'ai' in 'hail'.
ee sounds like the 'ee' in 'sheep'.

igh and oa

Circle the letters **igh**. Underline the letters **oa**.
Then draw a line from a word to the correct picture.

| foam | right | toad | night |

Write **igh** or **oa** to complete each word.

| s__p | l___t | c__t |

igh sounds like the 'igh' in 'night'.
oa sounds like the 'oa' in 'boat'.

oo and oo

Colour the balls with the **oo** sound (as in 'loop') red.
Colour the balls with the *oo* sound (as in 'look') blue.
Then write your own **oo** word and *oo* word in the blank balls.

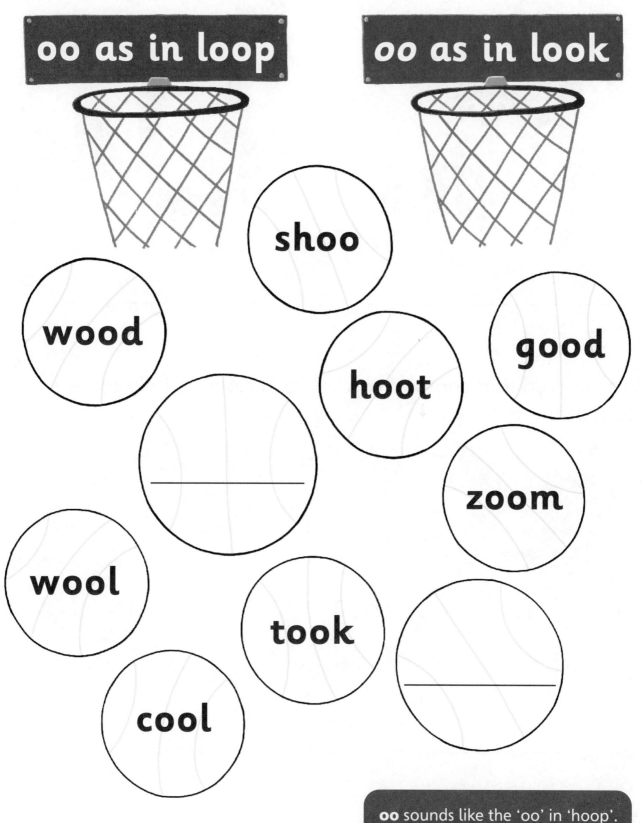

oo as in loop

oo as in look

shoo

wood

hoot

good

zoom

wool

took

cool

Write the word containing **ai**.

_____

Write the word containing **ee**.

_____

Write a word that contains **igh** on each cloud to help Rosie zoom across the sky.

Colour the picture and then write the **oo** or **oo** word.

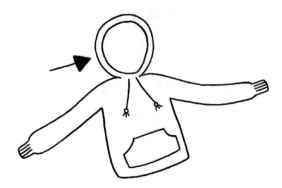

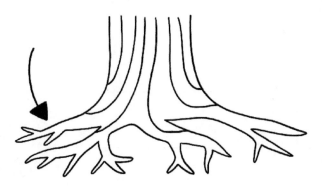

_____   _____

How many **oa** words can you see? Write the words in the boxes.

c_____   c_____

t_____   r_____

Fill in the blanks

Write **oa** words to complete the sentence.

The _____ is
on a _____ .

Write **ee** words to complete the sentence.

The _____ beeps
at the _____ .

Write **oo** words to complete the sentences.

Max is a _____ .

He has a _____ .

Writing sentences

Now write your own sentences about the pictures, using the focus sounds.

oo

_____

ee ai

_____

oa

_____

ar and or

Help Anika find the right bus stops. Colour the stops with an **ar** word red and the bus stops with an **or** word green.
Then write your own **ar** word and **or** word in the blank bus stops.

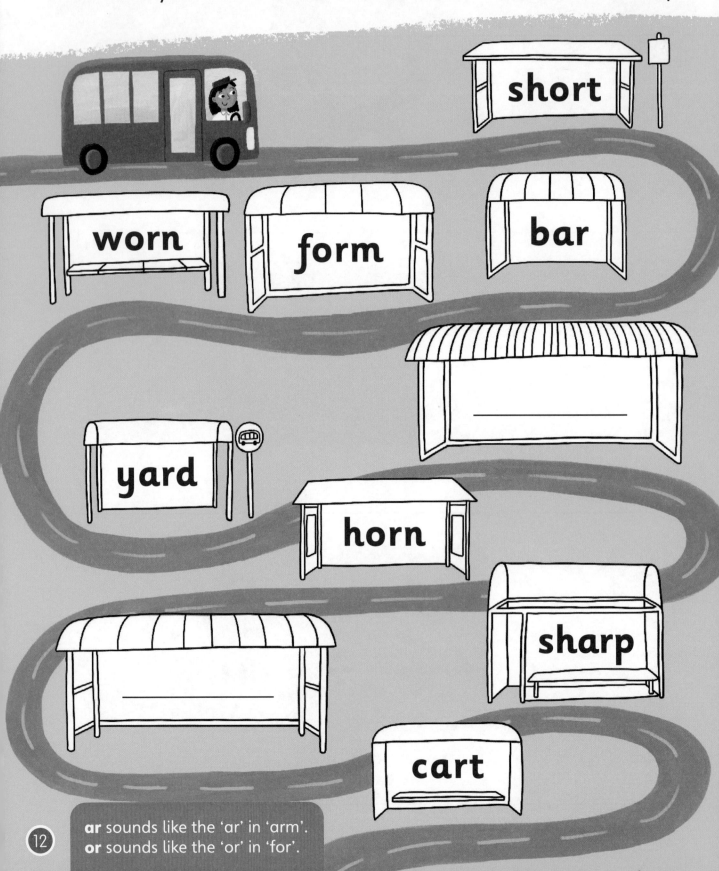

short

worn

form

bar

yard

horn

sharp

cart

ar sounds like the 'ar' in 'arm'.
or sounds like the 'or' in 'for'.

Sid Squirrel only likes eating tasty brown acorns.
Help him by colouring the acorns with an **ur** word green and
the acorns with an **ow** word brown.

Write each **ur** or **ow** word.

_____ _____

ur sounds like the 'ur' in 'curl'.
ow sounds like the 'ow' in 'how'.

oi and ear

All the ducklings have got muddled up. Help the mother ducks to find their ducklings by colouring in the ducklings with an **oi** word yellow and the ducklings with an **ear** word blue. Then write your own **oi** word and **ear** word in the blank ducklings.

oil

ear

oi

join

toil

avoid

dear

year

gear

near

oi sounds like the 'oi' in 'soil'.
ear sounds like the 'ear' in 'hear'.

Colour stepping stones to spell each word and hop across the river. Then write the word on the line.

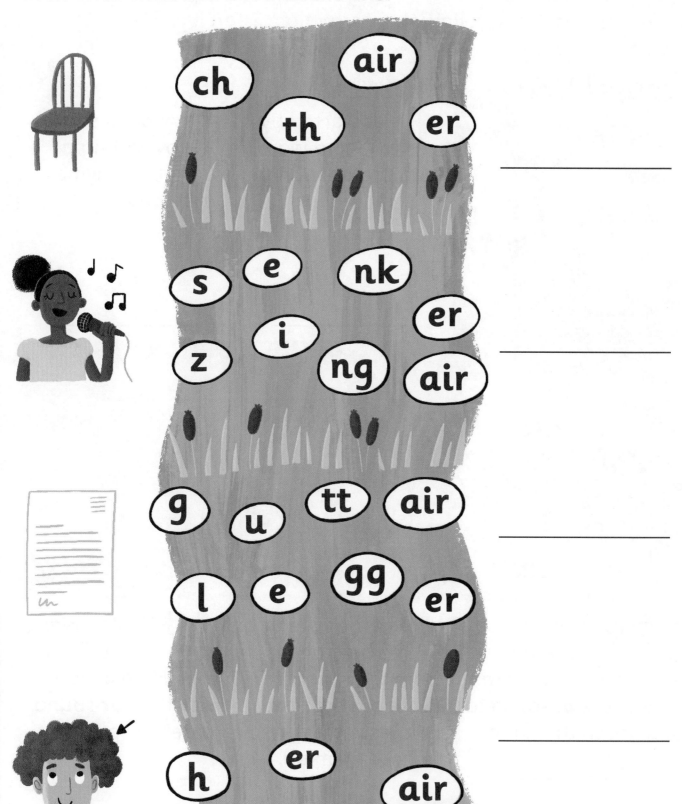

air sounds like the 'air' in 'fair'.
er sounds like the 'er' in 'better'.

15

Racetrack word game

Be the first to scoot around the track. You will need a dice and a counter for each player (one or more players). Throw the dice, move on and follow the instruction. Then it is the next person's turn.

START!

1 Get started by writing a word with the **ar** sound.

_____

2 Avoid a stone by writing a word that rhymes with '**pow**'.

_____

A chequered flag

FINISH LINE!

14 Write a word with the **ow** sound and a word with the **oi** sound to scoot to the finish.

_____

13 Your friend has fallen from their scooter! Write a word that rhymes with '**turn**' to help them up.

_____

12 You're nearly at the finish line! Write a word with the **ear** sound to get closer.

_____

4 Have a break! Write a letter to make this into a word.

_ork

5 Write a word with the **ear** sound to keep moving.

_____

6 A bird swoops too low. Write two words that rhyme to avoid it.

_____

_____

3 Write a word with the **ur** sound to speed up. Then move on three spaces.

_____

7 Write an **air** word to make your scooter go faster.

_____

8 Write a word that rhymes with '**coin**' to swerve around the corner.

_____

11 Write two words with the **er** sound to avoid a puddle.

_____

_____

10 Write a word that rhymes with '**fair**' to make your wheels turn faster.

_____

9 You're over halfway round the track! Write two **ar** words.

_____

_____

Word castle

Write the **or**, **ow** and **ar** words in the boxes.

Write a sentence with one of the words in.

_____

The sentence robot has a problem! Help the robot explain what happened by using the words from the box to make a sentence.

fell arm my off

_____

_____

_____

Now write a sentence using some of the words from the box to say how to fix the robot.

to hit hammer it back join with the on

_____

_____

Tricky words

Complete each sentence using the words in the box.
Then draw a line from each sentence to the correct picture.

are   was   my   all

This is _____ book.

Dev can pick up _____ of his cars.

I _____ at the park this morning.

The cats _____ waiting for dinner.

Stop the nonsense words!

Help the goalkeeper stop the balls by drawing a line through the nonsense words.

sharp

year

burn

harg

goam

right

jairn

wood

vain

worn

zeen

Coded messages

Josh and Alfie have sent each other notes.
Write the word for each picture to work out what they say.

Can you meet in the

_____ ?

It looks like it will

_____ .

We can put on

_____ .

Yes! I will put on my

_____ too!

Crossword

Use the clues to help you to do the crossword.
One has been done for you.

Across

2.

4.

5.

8. ✔

Down

1.

3.

5.

6.

7.

8. m o o n

Well done!

You have completed
Phonics Workbook
Book 3

Name: ....

Age: ....

Date: ....